CW00406620

"This is a delightful book
on firm evidence about \
    when preparing for chi
page of the book has a simple practice that invites you
to meet each moment with openness and stability in
the midst of everything."

MARK WILLIAMS
CO-AUTHOR OF MINDFULNESS:
FINDING PEACE IN A FRANTIC WORLD

"What a wonderfully straightforward and easily understand-
able introduction to mindfulness practice for parents-to-
be. Suffused with kindness and grounded in research, any
expectant parent can begin to reap the benefits of becoming
more mindful by reading these pages and then choosing to
practice something offered within."

NANCY BARDACKE
AUTHOR OF MINDFUL BIRTHING

"A practical and accessible introduction to the value of
mindfulness during pregnancy, beautifully written and pre-
sented. A gift for all parents to be."

DR MARET DYMOND-BASSETT
CLINICAL PSYCHOLOGIST & TUTOR
ON THE UNIVERSITY OF OXFORD
MASTER OF STUDIES IN MBCT

"An inspiring "how to guide" for a calm and mindful pregnancy. This book provides a simple toolkit for parents to find mindful moments in the journey of parenthood. Every page has a gem of mindfulness to practise. I imagine it becoming a well thumbed source as parents turn to it over again."

KATE BUCHANAN
REGISTERED MIDWIFE AND COUNSELLOR, MINDFUL PREGNANCY BIRTH EDUCATION, PERTH, WESTERN AUSTRALIA
WWW.MINDFULPREGNANCY.COM.AU

"This delightful book taps into the wisdom of mindfulness through simple practices that any busy parent-to-be can easily manage. It provides accessible mindfulness to support expectant parents in connecting with themselves, their baby and each other. With gentle and clear guidance, expectant parents will discover practical ways to bring more calm, peace and connection into the experience of pregnancy and early parenting. It's a gem and I'll be recommending it to all the expectant parents I work with."

BECCA CALHOUN
MPH, NORTHWEST MINDFUL BIRTHING & PARENTING, SEATTLE

"Simple and concise, based on solid research. I wish more pregnancy books were like this."

HESTER P.
MOTHER OF TWO, LONDON

HOW TO HAVE
A MINDFUL PREGNANCY

30 tried and tested, simple ways to connect with
your baby and your body

SIAN WARRINER
AND MARK PALLIS

NEU WESTEND
— PRESS —

For the women who have taught me,
my MBCP friends and colleagues.

Sian Warriner

For Benedetta with love.

Mark Pallis

How to have a mindful pregnancy

30 tried and tested, simple ways to
connect with your baby and your body

By Sian Warriner and Mark Pallis

Design and layout by Klara Block

Disclaimer: All reasonable care has been
taken in the preparation of this book.
Any information given in this book is not
to be taken as a replacement for medical
advice from your qualified medical
practitioner. Any person with a medical
condition should consult their doctor
before trying the exercises in this book.

First Printing, 2019

ISBN 978-1-9160801-0-2

NeuWestendPress.com

CONTENTS

JUST AS YOU ARE

A wise midwife once described the joys and challenges of pregnancy and birth to me as transformational: a moment in time when our lives change for ever. She was right. The occasion of pregnancy, birth and becoming a parent is frequently a time when we take stock and choose to make intentional, positive changes and mindfulness can be incredibly helpful with this. This book offers thirty simple ways that you, as a mum-to-be who still has to navigate day-to-day life, can bring mindfulness into your pregnancy, just as you are.

WHY MINDFULNESS?

Mindfulness is the practice of bringing your attention to what is happening in the present moment. It could be your breath, the sensations in your body, your emotions, almost anything. The key is to intentionally experience the present moment, non-judgmentally and with kindness and self-compassion. Just be in it as best you can.

Over the past two decades, the practice of mindfulness has evolved from its Eastern meditation roots to a mainstream, secular and increasingly accessible way of supporting our mental health and emotional wellbeing. We now have strong, scientifically robust evidence that a regular meditation practice can shift us from a place where we may feel overwhelmed, stressed or out of control to a calmer and more contented headspace.

As a Consultant Midwife leading Oxford University Hospitals NHS Foundation Trust's Mindfulness-Based Childbirth and Parenting antenatal education programme and an Associate at the Oxford Mindfulness Centre, it's my privilege to introduce pregnant women and their families to mindfulness. I also teach mindfulness courses to healthcare professionals, Oxford University staff and the public.

Everyone's experience of pregnancy is different. Nevertheless, I've seen first-hand how mindfulness can provide the tools to navigate the wonderful yet demanding time that is pregnancy. Rather than simply 'getting through it', with mindfulness we can thrive and become fully present for all of the ups and downs this time holds. We can develop a set of simple yet hugely powerful skills that can transform our emotional experience and wellbeing.

BUT DOES MINDFULNESS ACTUALLY HELP DURING PREGNANCY?

I recently led a research team studying the effects of mindfulness in pregnancy, birth and into parenthood (Warriner et al, 2018). Our study demonstrated that using mindfulness techniques in pregnancy has the potential to reduce pregnancy-related worry and allow space for life to be 'just as it is'. This builds self-compassion, inner calm and ease, making mothers feel more connected to their bodies and to the whole experience of pregnancy.

We also found that mindfulness can support us in developing our relationship with ourselves, our partner and baby for the better. In particular, we found a significant increase in both expectant parents' wellbeing. Women demonstrated a significant improvement in symptoms of stress, anxiety, depression, pregnancy-related distress and labour worry. Partners too showed significant progress in managing anxiety and depression, and showed a trend for improvement in self-reported symptoms of perceived stress.

Other studies have even shown that mindfulness can help take the sting out of a bad night's sleep for mums-to-be (Felder et al, 2017). Others have underlined the positive, stress-reducing effect of mindfulness in pregnancy and shown that being relaxed in pregnancy is good for you and good for your baby too (Newman et al, 2017; Duncanand Bardacke, 2010).

USING THIS BOOK

This book is deliberately short. It draws on exercises that I use regularly in my teaching. Each one has been designed to be as straightforward as possible and to fit into even the busiest lifestyles.

You can choose how you want to use the book. To begin, I suggest that you simply set aside a moment in the day to intentionally practice, then pick any exercise that feels right for you and follow the guidance on the page.

Mindfulness is simple and once you become more familiar with the exercises, you'll start to develop your own natural flow. You may then like to try extending your intentional practice to ten or ideally twenty minutes each day. If this feels like an unrealistic target for you, just do what you can and you will still benefit. As you progress, you can use your mindfulness skills at different moments throughout your day as a way of reconnecting with the present moment, your body and your baby.

So, take the time to be present, slow down, reflect and use this book and the skills it offers as a gift to yourself. I wish you all the very best for your pregnancy and beyond.

Sian

THE
BEAUTY
OF YOUR
BREATH

Sitting and quietly focusing on breathing has been used for centuries as a way to meditate and centre ourselves. It has also been used by midwives for generations as a way to encourage calm and ease during labour. And it's perfect in pregnancy too.

We all know that breathing comes so naturally – we can do it in our sleep. That's why gently bringing our attention to our breath as we breathe in and out is such a powerful process. It's like a metronome that never stops, something we can use as an anchor to the present moment.

The effect on our bodies as we slow down and focus on our breath is profound. As we intentionally bring our awareness to the breath, mindfulness offers us the possibility to step back from the usual chatter of our busy minds, to make space to settle and to notice. Our pulse rate slows and we create the opportunity to feel more present.

It might seem very simple but that's the beauty of your breath: it's always there for you. Any time that you feel you need 'a moment', you can take a few breaths and bring your attention to the present.

That's the essence of mindfulness.

MY FIRST
MINDFUL
BREATHS

If you've never tried mindfulness before, the easiest way to start is by taking a couple of intentionally long breaths. It's a bit like squeezing the brakes on a bike – it slows you right down.

Sit comfortably and then breathe in, for longer than normal. Breathe out and then take another long breath in. That's it, you've started.

BREATHE
WITH BABY

When you notice baby move, place your left
hand on your belly and your right hand on your
heart. Now, focus your attention on baby and take a
moment to simply be with the breath and your baby.

TIP

This is a wonderful way for you to build a sense of
connection between yourself and your baby. It doesn't
matter where you are or what you're doing; when
you feel movement, you can use it as a cue to take a
moment to connect.

COUNTING BREATHS:

NINE IS JUST FINE

Breathe in and out nine times – one breath for each month of a pregnancy. You can count on your fingers so that you don't lose track. As you breathe, reflect on your baby growing with each passing month.

TIP

This is great if you only have a small amount of time. Pausing and intentionally being present for just nine breaths can help create space and the opportunity for calm. It's totally normal for your mind to wander or to lose track of which number you are up to. If that happens, don't worry, just start again.

Get comfortable. Next, bring your awareness to the feeling of the air coming into your nose, up into your nostrils, flowing over the back of your throat and then down into your lungs.

As you breathe in, notice any pleasant or less comfortable sensations around your baby bump as your rib cage lifts up and out, and then as it gently falls back when you breathe out. Feel the exhalation coming up from your lungs and out of your mouth. That's one breath.

Repeat for as long as it feels right for you. Perhaps five minutes.

DANCING
CANDLE

Light a candle and watch the flame as you centre yourself with a couple of breaths.

Now, gently exhale and notice the way your breath makes the flame dance.

TIP

Some mothers like to recall this image as their baby is being born, to remind them that pushes can be gentle, as well as powerful.

FINGER
BREATHING

As you inhale, use a finger to gently trace a line from the palm of your left hand up to the tip of one finger. As you exhale, press the tip of that finger. Now, repeat with all ten fingers.

TIP
Take a moment to notice the sensations on your palm, as well as of your breath.

ALL
FIVE
SENSES

Like our breath, our body is always in the present moment. Our minds tend to get drawn into the past or future, whereas our body is always here. Our senses give us a way of fully engaging with our present experience and using our senses is a key part of mindful practice. As we connect with sensation, our attention is gently drawn away from thoughts and thinking, allowing us to settle in the present moment. One effect of being more present is that it allows us to sense, connect with and appreciate the small things which we often overlook.

Our body's five senses affect our emotions. For example, tuning into our sense of touch is an easy and effective way of activating our resting and regenerating state. Our sympathetic and parasympathetic nervous systems work hand-in-hand to control our physical and emotional states. The sympathetic system is responsible for our 'fight or flight response' to fears or threats – releasing adrenaline which causes our heart rate to rise and breathing to shallow. On the other hand, when the parasympathetic nervous system is activated, it produces a calm and relaxed feeling in the mind and body. We can learn to trigger this response by breathing deeply and mindfully or tuning into our senses, such as touch. For example, our lips have parasympathetic fibres spread throughout them, so lightly running a finger over them activates our parasympathetic nervous system, increasing a sense of wellbeing.

Once you're familiar with becoming more aware of your senses and body, let this awareness become your daily practice.

SENSATIONAL
SHOWER

Even something as simple as paying attention to the sensations we experience when showering is enough to trigger the parasympathetic nervous system.

While you shower, take a moment to notice the sensation of the water on your skin and hair. Listen to all the different sounds it makes; watch it trickle down the shower screen. Pay close attention to your baby bump and notice all the sensations of the bubbles from the soap or shampoo.

TIP

Try a caring gesture, like putting your hand on any discomfort in your body. Caress it gently, in the same way that you will ease and soothe your baby as a loving parent.

LOTION
WITHOUT
COMMOTION

Next time you put your favourite lotion on
your bump, take a moment to really notice all
sensations: the feeling of opening the cream, of
squeezing it out onto your hands, the sensation as
your hands touch your bump and how that feeling
subtly changes as the cream is absorbed. Notice
too, the texture and tone of the bump.

TIP

Making time for some self-care every day, like putting
some cream on your bump, is a great way to slow
down and relax.

MINDFUL WALKING

When we walk, we are often on autopilot. We focus on our destination or things that we need to get done and have little awareness of what is going on around us or in our bodies.

We can use the sensations of walking to provide a connection to the present moment. This allows us to slow down, create steadiness, composure and reconnect with a sense of mindful presence.

As you walk, notice how your body feels. Feel the contact of your foot as it touches the ground. Notice the solidity of the earth beneath your feet. Notice the movement of your body as you move into your next step. Pay attention to how your legs, feet and arms feel with each step you take. With openness and curiosity, notice any sensations, thoughts or feelings that arise, without lingering on anything in particular. And while you're out and about, you can help stay in the moment by, for example, touching the bark of a tree, smelling a flower or engaging with anything else you see that triggers your senses.

TIP

Intentional, mindful walking can be very useful when settling a crying baby. They will pick up on your heart rate and so, the more relaxed you are, the more relaxed they will be too.

AMAZING
RAISIN

It's amazing how the simple act of paying attention and truly being present can transform an experience for us. You can do this exercise with anything you eat – chocolate is also a popular choice!

LOOK at the raisin. Notice the colour, areas of light and shade, any ridges or shine.

TOUCH the raisin. Explore the raisin's texture with your fingers. Is the skin waxy? It is soft or hard?

SMELL the raisin. Bring it close to your nose and notice any scent; has this triggered your taste buds? While you're doing this, if thoughts arise such as, "This feels really odd," see if you can simply acknowledge these thoughts without having to act on them or change them.

HEAR the sounds. Bring the raisin to one ear, squeeze it, roll it around, notice if there is any sound coming from it.

TASTE the raisin. Place it in your mouth but don't chew yet. How does the raisin feel on your tongue? Take a bite without swallowing. How does it taste? Notice your intention to swallow it and follow the physical action.

Now take a moment to notice how your whole body feels.

TIP

When your baby is born, you can notice every little detail of their toes, fingers, skin texture, the softness, the smell. It's a wonderful technique to encourage connection and bonding.

BODY SCAN

Sit or lie comfortably with pillows to support your bump. Close your eyes and bring your awareness to your body as a whole, feeling its weight and points of contact. Take a few deep breaths, noticing the sensations of breathing in your nose, throat, chest and abdomen.

Now slowly bring your attention down to your toes, noticing all the sensations that might be there – cold, warmth, tingling, heaviness, or no sensation at all.

When you are ready, move your attention up to your feet, ankles, calves, knees and thighs. As best you can, gently notice the sensations you are experiencing without judgement. Slowly work your way up your body: pelvis, lower back, abdomen, chest, upper back, shoulders, arms, neck, head and face. Be curious about the sensations. See if it is possible to softly breathe into any area of discomfort and allow a sense of softening and ease as you breathe out. If you notice your mind wandering off, gently gather your attention and return to noticing the sensations in your body. Finally, imagine sending your breath all the way down to your feet and then back up again as if your whole body were breathing.

TIP

It is common to feel tired or fall asleep during a body scan, in fact some people use it as a way of getting back to sleep if they wake at night. No matter what happens, try approaching the experience with a sense of kindness and compassion towards yourself – there is no right or wrong way to do it.

This exercise is designed for all of the senses to be used in one sitting and is a wonderful way to give your baby information about the world she or he will be born into.

Notice five things that you can see.
Bring your attention to things that give a sense of the beauty of the world and what you want your baby to see.

Notice four things that you can feel.
Bring awareness to things that you are currently feeling. Perhaps it's your clothes, the feeling of the breeze on your skin, or the softness of a baby blanket.

Notice three things you can hear.
Identify and listen to different sounds in the
background. Maybe it's birdsong, the sound of
rain, or a favourite piece of music.

Notice two things you can smell.
Bring your awareness to smells. Perhaps coffee or
if you're outside, the smell of flowers or grass.

Notice one thing you can taste.
Focus on something that you can taste right now,
in this moment. You can take a sip of a drink,
eat something, or just notice the current taste
in your mouth.

IN
THE
MOMENT

Well-wishing words
Breath hug for baby
Baby's first lullaby
Baby's first story
Gratitude is good
Mindful Mountain

Visualisation is one of the practices used in mindful-ness meditation.

When you focus your attention on something in your mind's eye, you're visualising. Visualisation can be used to enhance attitudes that are associated with mindfulness, like non-judging, patience, curiosity, trust, non-striving, accepting and letting go. We choose an image – a mountain is often used in mindfulness – and then we reflect on what that image suggests and how it makes us feel. Some of the more common responses include stillness, strength, stability or beauty.

We can then use our sense of these qualities to provide grounding, inner strength and calm. This gives us a different approach to experiencing the present moment. And in terms of the effect on our bodies, meditation decreases the production of the stress hormones cortisol and adrenaline and gives baby a signal that they are safe and protected.

Repeating special words or phrases (sometimes called mantras) is a simple and effective way to begin the practice of meditation and helps build capacity for self-compassion and kindness.

Sit comfortably, with one hand on your bump and one on your heart and repeat these words out loud:

May you be happy and healthy
May you be safe and protected
May you live in peace and with kindness.

You can use your own words too. The important thing is to softly and gently speak the words for as long as it feels comfortable, perhaps a couple of minutes to start with.

TIP
You can also use your mantra words for yourself, a loved one, a community of people or everyone.

Place one hand on your belly and the other hand
on your heart. Take a moment to relax. As you
breathe in, imagine your breath flowing down and
around your baby as if you were wrapping them
in a blanket. Imagine it nourishing baby as you
breathe in and hugging baby as you breathe out.

Visualise baby feeling loved and safe and warm.

Your baby's hearing is developing all the time; from about 23 weeks they can hear your heart-beat. They will also start to hear sounds from the outside world. Hearing your voice during your pregnancy helps your baby to feel attached to you when they are born.

Visualise your baby, either by looking at a scan or putting your hands on your bump. Then sing as much, or as little, of a song as you like. Baby will hear the soft vibrations of your voice and, if you sing the same song once they're born, they will recognise it and should find it comforting.

TIP
Singing has been shown to have a calming effect on the singer too. Everybody wins!

Choose a story that you love and sit comfortably.
Then simply read it to your bump. As you read,
really try to imagine your baby, whether it's their
squidgy thighs or the sensation of what it will
feel like when they grab your finger. If you can
manage to read the story regularly, baby will
become accustomed to your voice – the most
significant sound they'll hear while in your womb.
Research shows that babies' heart rates slow when
you speak – they find it calming.

TIP

This is especially useful for partners because it helps
them imagine baby and begins to build a bond for
them too.

Science tells us that gratitude has a profound effect on our brains, improving our sense of wellbeing by increasing the release of dopamine and oxytocin, our feel-good hormones.

As you relax, bring to mind five things that you are grateful for. Ideally, they should be connected to your baby and your experience of pregnancy. Count them off on your fingers. Once you have all five, quietly reflect on them, letting yourself sit with the sensation of feeling grateful.

TIP

Reflecting on positive feelings – such as gratitude – during pregnancy is worthwhile because it helps us notice things that we might otherwise overlook, when we are overwhelmed with physical or emotional discomfort or even the simple all encompassing nature of pregnancy. It's totally fine if you can't think of anything you're grateful for or if other feelings, such as sadness, come up. You're not doing it wrong; simply bring your attention back to your breath and the present moment.

Bring your attention to your breath. Imagine
you are gazing at a beautiful, mighty mountain.
You are warm and relaxed. You are holding your
sleeping baby in your arms. The mountain stands
solidly and peacefully in front of you and in the
same way, you can feel calm and settled.

As you breathe in and out, allow a deep sense of
relaxation and a feeling of love to envelop you
and your baby. It cocoons you both and makes
you feel safe.

Just as the mountain will endure, so will your
love: unchanging, unwavering, rock solid. Forever.

TIP

In practising the mindful mountain meditation, we
can learn to embody the same centred, unwavering
stillness and groundedness in the face of all that
changes in our life – over seconds, hours and years.

CONNECT
TO
THE
PRESENT

Being mindful doesn't always involve sitting still. You can bring your attention to the present moment in many ways, including by intentionally focusing on a particular task.

For parents-to-be, turning ordinary activities into mindful activities is a great way of adding some mindful practice to a daily routine. It's also a useful way to introduce mindfulness if you or your partner feel uncomfortable, or perhaps unsure, about sitting and focussing on your breath.

What matters is to be in the present moment – how you get there is less important. A recent study used neuro-imaging techniques showed the effect that mindfulness practice has on the brain. The study mapped activity in the brain and showed that it enhanced attention, improved emotion regulation and reduced stress. The changes in our brains are not simply emotional but physical. An extensive review in 2015, which looked at the current state of neuroscience research, found emerging evidence that 'mindfulness meditation was associated with neuroplastic changes in the structure and function of brain regions involved in regulation of attention, emotion and self-awareness' (Tang, 2015).

With regular practice these changes can provide a more open, creative and ultimately more enjoyable life experience.

Do you sometimes find that being pregnant makes it a bit more difficult to do things as quickly as you did before? That's great – go with it!

Whatever you are doing, deliberately slow it down and reflect on how it feels. It could be anything: eating, walking, tidying up, stroking a pet, even reading this book. As we slow down, we notice the present moment much more. Whatever feelings come up, just notice and – as best you can – accept them without judging. Then, gently bring your attention back to the present.

Create a visual representation of what being a parent means to you. You can do this using online tools like Pinterest, or you can do it the 'old-fashioned' way, cutting out images from magazines, and arranging them on a big sheet of paper.

As you contemplate each image that you include in your collection, take a moment to identify why it resonates with you and how it makes you feel.

TIP

You can share your finished board with friends or family and use it to start a conversation. This is also a great activity for partners.

Yoga benefits mums-to-be in all kinds of ways; it helps your body by promoting muscle strength and tone, getting you ready for the physical demands of birth. And, more than that, it provides time to relax, helping reduce stress and encouraging a connection to the body. If your doctor hasn't advised you otherwise, consider visiting a local class or try the classic 'wide-knee child's pose' which is a wonderfully soothing way to take the pressure off your back.

Kneel on the ground, with the tops of your feet on the floor and your bottom gently resting on your heels. Make your knees wider than hip-width apart and allow space for your bump. Gently bring your chest down to the floor, letting your belly come between your legs. Extend your arms in front of you, with your forehead resting on the floor. You can support your forehead or chest with a folded blanket, particularly in the later stages of pregnancy.

TIP

As you hold the pose, be present and notice the sensations in your body. It's fine if your mind wanders off; simply bring your attention back to the present moment, non-judgmentally and with kindness.

If your day is particularly great, particularly tough, or even particularly average, take a moment to reflect on your feelings and note them down. You can write about what you are feeling and also about the sensations that those feelings create in your body. This helps us untangle facts from emotions, which in turn can promote a sense of ease. Understanding that our thoughts are not permanent but are passing mental events that shift and change just as life does, is another element of bringing mindfulness into our daily lives.

Taken together, your collection of notes will create a rich record of your pregnancy. It can be rewarding to look back through it once your pregnancy is over, reflecting on your experience and taking a moment to congratulate yourself.

MUMMY'S TUMMY

Documenting your growing bump is an excellent way to help build the bond between mum-to-be and baby. You can take photos, draw sketches, or even just regularly observe your bump. The key is to spend a moment or two reflecting on your changing body and the baby growing inside you – it truly is miraculous.

When your baby gets active and gives a little kick, you can use that as a cue for some mindfulness. You can try a few 'breath hugs', or you can play-fully give your belly a gentle rub or a little nudge and imagine you're giving baby a high five. It's fun and even a small smile or chuckle from you will trigger dopamine, endorphins and serotonin, making you feel happy and calm – baby will feel it too.

FOR BOTH OF YOU

Make something for the baby
Shared well-wishing mantra
Day-to-day mindfulness
Chill out, literally
Speak and listen, mindfully
Once the baby is born …

Partners play a crucial role supporting mums-to-be, so looking out for a partner's mental wellbeing can have a very positive impact on a household. Research shows that when partners practised mindful activities, they saw significant improvements in symptoms of anxiety and depression, as well as a trend for improvement in self-reported symptoms of perceived stress.

Partners can do almost all of the activities in this book. In the pages that follow, you will find some exercises that are designed for you to do together. Whether it is sharing a special moment or simply contemplating the magic of what you have created, these exercises aim to strengthen the bonds between you both, and between your partner and baby too.

Almost anything can be done mindfully; all you need to do is slow down and intentionally focus your attention on the present moment. Why not try some of these shared activities:

»   Look for a special item of clothing for baby. Really hold them in your mind as you choose and visualise them wearing it.

»   Pick a book for baby that has special meaning to you from your childhood and reflect on how you will feel, sharing it with your own child.

»   Go through some items from your own childhood and select something that has special meaning to pass on to your own child.

»   Sit together with your partner holding hands and engage in some mindful breathing.

MAKE SOMETHING
FOR BABY

As you work, picture yourselves being together with baby, enjoying whatever it is that you are making. This process of painting a mental picture builds the sense of connection between you and baby.

Ideas to try: Decorate baby's room or area, assemble their cot, decorate a picture frame, write a special poem, make a belly cast.

TIP

If you are working on a longer project, like decorating baby's room, try focusing on doing it mindfully for set periods, say for five minutes at a time.

SHARED WELL-WISHING MANTRA

Sitting together, both place one hand on the baby bump and the other hand on your own heart.

You can choose your own special words, or say:

Welcome to family
Welcome to love
Welcome to happiness.
Welcome to our lives.

This exercise is adapted from the ice practice described by Nancy Bardacke in her book *Mindful Birthing*.

Put some ice cubes in a bowl. Take a moment to become still, bringing your attention to the sensation of your breath as it comes in and out. After a minute, both take a handful of ice cubes. Notice what happens in your mind and on your skin. If it becomes uncomfortable at any point, put the ice down and gently warm your hands.

Consider the sensations: there's the cold stinging, and there's also the slow trickle and tickle of the ice as it melts. Pay attention to the story your mind is telling you about the sensations and notice any emotional responses you have.

TIP

This exercise encourages couples to 'be with' discomfort, exploring what it truly feels like, rather than what we thought it would feel like. While intense sensations might not change too much, with mindful attention our relationship with them will likely shift, like the contraction we thought would last forever but actually waxes and wanes in spells of intensity. As is often quoted: "Pain is inevitable, suffering is optional."

SPEAK AND LISTEN, MINDFULLY

Each person thinks of one thing that worries them about becoming a parent and one thing they are looking forward to.

Each person takes turns in sharing what they have thought of, without the need for their partner to respond or feel the need to jump in and 'fix' anything.

Both partners observe their own thoughts, feelings and body sensations when talking and when listening.

Both partners direct their attention to how it feels to talk about something they are worried about, as well as how it feels to share something positive.

TIP

People often find this mindful approach to sharing their feelings a useful way to talk about issues they find difficult, or about feelings more generally.

ONCE YOUR
BABY IS BORN

Once your baby is born, take a moment to mindfully observe all the tiny details about them: their hair, their smell, the folds of their skin, their tiny fingernails. And observe your own feelings as well. The child is a wonder, and so are you.

FURTHER READING

Here are some more resources about mindfulness. This book does not include exercises for labour, as this is a specialised area that needs a whole book to itself, but see below for helpful advice and contacts.

BOOKS

Mindful Birthing by Nancy Bardacke (HarperOne 2012)
Expecting Mindfully by Sona Dimidjian and Sheryl H. Goodman (Taylor & Francis Ltd, 2019)
The Headspace Guide to a Mindful Pregnancy by Andy Puddicombe (Hodder, 2017)
Mindfulness: A Practical Guide to Finding Peace in a Frantic World by Mark Williams and Danny Penman (Piatkus Books, 2011)

APPS

Frantic World App:
franticworld.com/mindfulness-apps/
Oxford Mindfulness Centre Mindfulness App:
oxfordmindfulness.org/insight/oxford-mbct-app/
Headspace:
headspace.com/headspace-meditation-app

WEBSITES AND GROUPS

Oxford Mindfulness Centre: oxfordmindfulness.o
Mindful: mindful.org
Headspace: headspace.com
Action for Happiness: actionforhappiness.org
Breathworks: breathworks-mindfulness.org.uk
Mindfulness in Schools Project:
mindfulnessinschools.org

REFERENCES

Duncan, L.G. and Bardacke, N., 'Mindfulness-Based Childbirth and Parenting Education: Promoting Family Mindfulness During the Perinatal Period', *Journal of Child and Family Studies*. 19:2 (2010) pp. 190–202

Felder, J.N., Laraia, B., Coleman-Phox, K., Bush, N., Suresh, M., Thomas, M., Adler, N., Epel, E., Prather, A., 'Poor Sleep Quality, Psychological Distress, and the Buffering Effect of Mindfulness Training During Pregnancy' *Behavioural Sleep Medicine*. 16:6 (2018) pp. 611-624.

Newman, L., Judd, F. and Komiti, A., 'Developmental Implications of Maternal Antenatal Anxiety Mechanisms and Approaches to Intervention', *Translational Developmental Psychiatry*, 5:1 (2017)

Tang, Y., K. Hölzel, B. K. and Posner, M.I., 'The Neuro-science of Mindfulness Meditation', *Nature Reviews, Neuroscience*. 16:4 (2015) pp. 213–225

Warriner S., Krusche A., Dymond M. and Crane, C., *An Evaluation of Mindfulness-Based Childbirth and Parenting Courses for Pregnant Women and Prospective Fathers/ Partners within the UK NHS* (MBCP-4-NHS). Midwifery, 64 (2018) pp. 1–10

Printed in Great
Britain
by Amazon